POPCORN SANDWICHES   #7

BROOM-HILDA

POPCORN SANDWICHES   #7

By Russell Myers

tempo
books

GROSSET & DUNLAP
A FILMWAYS COMPANY
Publishers • New York

RUSSELL MYERS

7/20

HI, BROOM-HILDA!

LET GO OF ME OR I'LL SUE YOU FOR EVERYTHING YOU'VE GOT!

I DON'T HAVE ANYTHING!

THEN I'LL BUY YOU A GIFT AND SUE YOU FOR IT!!

RUSSELL MYERS

IT'S HEARTWARMING TO HAVE A FRIEND WHO'LL GO OUT OF HER WAY FOR YOU!

7/29

RUSSELL MYERS

RUSSELL MYERS

This strip has
been condemned
by a group of very
serious citizens for
being much too
silly! MUCH!
Of all the nerve.
Snort. Harumph.

8/19

C'MON, IRWIN, GET *SERIOUS!*

RUSSELL
MYERS

FOING

THERE'S A BIG PARTY
TONIGHT SO I'M PRACTICING
MY FROG IMPRESSION!

8/24

RUSSELL MYERS

8/30

RUSSELL MYERS

RUSSELL MYERS

RUSSELL MYERS

9/9

RUSSELL MYERS

THE OLDER I GET, THE
MORE IT TAKES TO GET ME
GOIN' IN THE MORNIN'!

9-17

RUSSELL MYERS

THUD   PLOP   THUD

9-29

AN UGLY OLD WOMAN
ON A BROOM PUNCTURED
OUR DIRIGIBLE!

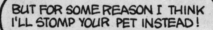

RUSSELL MYERS

WE'VE GOT ALL THE HITS TO GIVE YOU FITS! DOO-WAAAH!!!

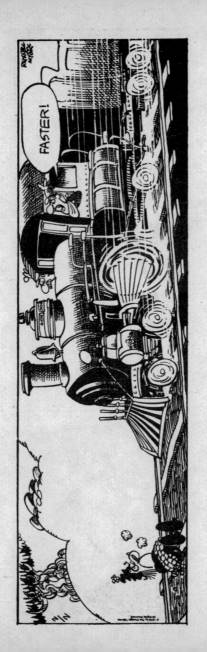

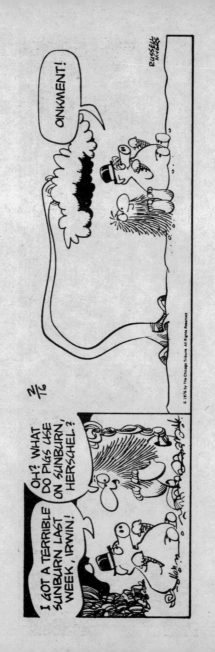

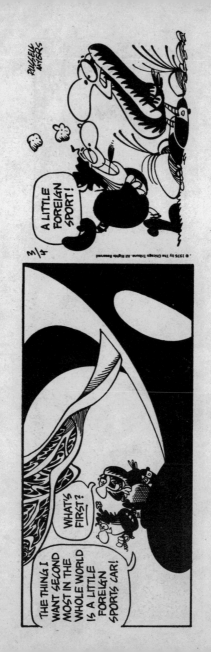

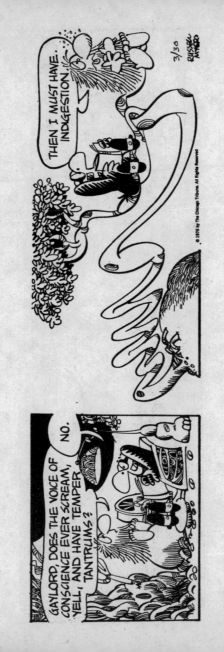

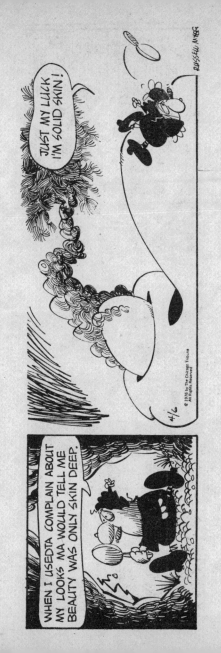

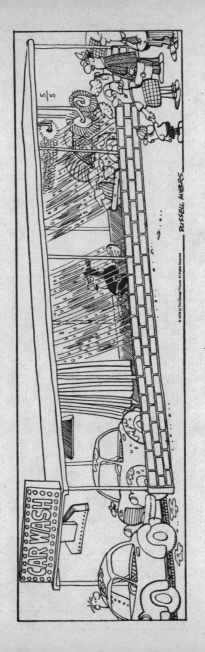

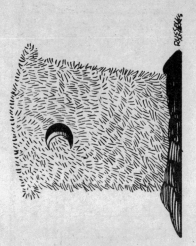

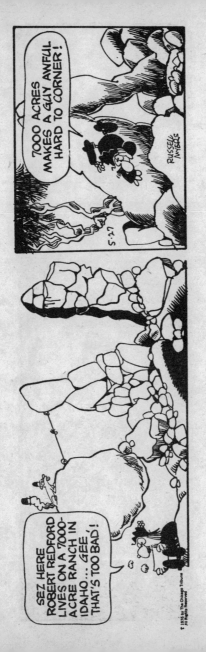

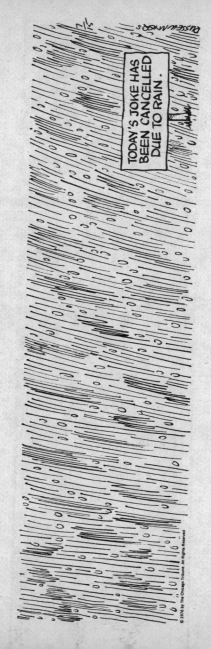

TODAY'S JOKE HAS
BEEN CANCELLED
DUE TO RAIN.

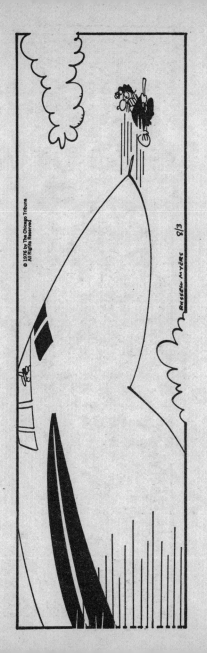

RUSSELL MYERS 9/3

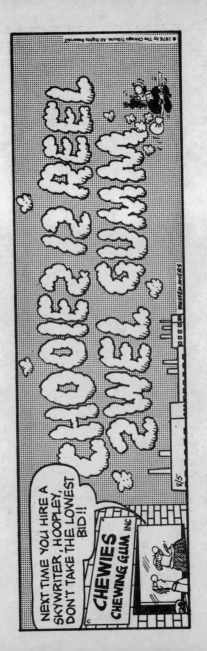

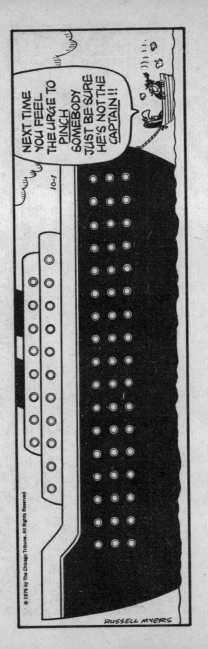